TELLING TALES

Sheila J. McMillan

ARTHUR H. STOCKWELL LTD
Torrs Park, Ilfracombe, Devon, EX34 8BA
Established 1898
www.ahstockwell.co.uk

First published in Great Britain, 2016

British Library Cataloguing-in-Publication Data.
A catalogue record for this book is available
from the British Library.

Proceeds from the sale of this book will go towards the Northern Ireland Branch of the Multiple Sclerosis Society.

ISBN 978-0-7223-4626-6
Printed in Great Britain by
Arthur H. Stockwell Ltd
Torrs Park Ilfracombe
Devon EX34 8BA

CONTENTS

BE YOURSELF

The evening arrived when I had to 'preside' over my first meeting of the Women's League. I was terrified. Earlier I had pleaded with my mother to continue on with the role following the death of my father, who had been the previous minister of the church for thirty years. However, she steadfastly refused on the grounds that she would be undermining my position as the new clergy wife. I harboured strong un-daughter-like feelings.

Most of the ladies gathered there had been part of my upbringing in the community where I played out my youth. Having only fleetingly observed my mother's efficient organisation of all the church activities during those years, I now felt utterly inadequate. She had always festooned our kitchen walls with lists of names, sandwich fillings and dates. The cake tins were always full of 'don't touch those, they are for the church' buns and biscuits, whereas I could barely boil an egg or sew on a button.

I felt the pressure of disapproving comparisons raining down on my head already as I walked over from the Manse to the church hall. I reminded myself that I had coped with every form of trauma in my day job as a social worker. Therefore, I could handle this . . . but still my knees wobbled and my hands sweated as I walked into the room. Being heavily pregnant did not enhance my outward image either. I looked round the room through a haze and felt every pair of eyes boring into my soul. With the now completely steamed-up glasses, I glimpsed my old school teacher, the local doctor and about twenty others of whom I was the youngest by about thirty years.

I stumbled clumsily to the front, trying to paste a look of intelligence onto my face.

A strange falsetto voice came out of my throat to an expectant silence: "Good evening, ladies. Tonight I want to thank . . ."

"Oh, wee Sheila!" a voice rang out from the back.

I recognised the mother of a childhood school friend, whose home had been a haven of home-baked soda bread and hot apple pies when we escaped there from the busy Manse.

"Isn't it just great to see you back here. Sure do you mind the time you and our Kathleen were caught progging the orchard and when you were jumping the hedge the apples fell down your school knickers?"

I winced.

There was a roar of laughter and suddenly everything was all right again. All hope of acting a dignified, sophisticated me disappeared.

In the nick of time, I had been justly reminded of my father's words of wisdom to me, on leaving home ten years earlier. "Just be kind and, above all, be yourself."

STRICTLY NO BALLROOM DANCING

"Forward, slide, together; forward, slide, together. Hold your arm up, Mr Jones. Don't look at your feet, Miss Bell. . . . Stop! Stop! How often must I tell you? This is a waltz, not a rugby scrum. Your bodies must move in time with your feet. And you do not clutch each other, you glide together. Now again, Betty, from the top. One, two, three. Forward, slide, together . . ."

I had just passed my Junior Certificate. In our family, the incentive was a bicycle for the eleven-plus examination, but formal dancing lessons for Junior Certificate. We attended an all-girls school so these were not just dancing steps; these were strides into the future and our first close encounters with boys.

Miss Lester of Lester's Dancing School saw herself as our protector.

She had strict rules about who would sit where and how often we could dance with the same partner and at what time we would leave for the bus stop outside, to ensure our unmolested return home. Juniors from seven to eight, seniors from eight to ten, and once a month a combined night with orange squash and biscuits. We were taught the fashionable dances of the day, the quickstep, the foxtrot, the waltz; and if we had been awfully good, we were allowed a turn at the terribly rakish South American samba.

Such classes were seen as an essential part of our upbringing. The final two years at school were littered with inter-school 'formals' so that we would learn how to conduct ourselves as young ladies. Northern Ireland's answer to finishing school in Switzerland. In our school it was deemed more important to know how to hold our knives and forks correctly than to win a university scholarship. We had to learn to pour a little salt onto the side of our plates and never to sprinkle it over the food, before we could practise to be a concert pianist. Hockey was tolerated, but deportment was compulsory.

The school formals were grand affairs. Mother made the dress – twenty-two yards of pale green tulle with diamanté shoulder straps – and Matron had to oversee a dress rehearsal in case anyone flaunted a strapless number or a see-through portion. Fathers ferried us there at eight and were instructed to return for us at eleven o'clock precisely. The only sin there was ever any time to commit was to have a quick puff of a shared fag in the girls' toilets. A sort of Palm Court Orchestra played bravely while the vice-principal dragged embarrassed young men from their huddle in one corner, across the candle-waxed ballroom floor to be introduced to some poor girl in the opposite corner who had not yet been asked onto the floor. The night was declared a success if we had acquired a male partner for the supper dance. If we had dallied round the floor more than twice with the one boy, we were branded as hussies! We glided round the gymnasium floors of most of those Belfast schools with an elegance that made Miss Lester very proud.

Some years later, I married into a small country town. As the outsider, I was under scrutiny and became the subject of much interest until the next victim came along. My husband thought that the best way to overcome this embarrassment was to put me on display, so to speak. Silence their curiosity or let the dogs see the hare and all that. An opportunity came at harvest time when the young farmers were having their annual dance. It was held in the local Orange Hall, which in those carefree days served as the local community hall. It was situated on Murphy's farmland, about 100 yards from their homestead and a mile up from the main road. What William did not think to mention was that the hall was accessed across a well-used cow field and that the only heating was from the pot-bellied stove, belching out black smoke amid spurts of flames from hell itself.

The dance was scheduled for eight o'clock so he and I arrived at five past. The hall was totally empty, so there was time to scrape off a couple of the layers of dung from my strappy high-heeled shoes before the rest arrived. An hour later, there were six of us: the farmer, the farmer's wife and her two strapping sons. They stood akimbo in front of the stove and stared me up and down without saying a word. They were smartly turned out in their Sunday suits, crisp white shirts and polished boots. Another hour passed before the band turned up. This was Joe with his accordion and Charley on the kettledrum that he dug out from below a pile of Orange regalia in the back corner. At eleven o'clock, the door opened again to admit a crowd of young people and the band struck up a tune at last. However, although they had all arrived together, once inside the men congregated against one wall, beside the stove, while the women grouped themselves at the opposite end near the toilet.

Three times the band played to an empty floor. The fourth time, one of Mrs Murphy's sons lurched towards me, having obviously been pushed forward by his mother. He stopped in front of me, stared at my feet and grunted, "Will ye hit the flure?"

He held me gingerly and then moved forward . . . onto my foot, then onto the toes. Next he landed a kick at the instep and another on an ankle bone while I smiled bravely determined to show I was enjoying his company. I tried to dodge the blows with occasional skips in the air, but they rained on mercilessly. The rhythm of the band was totally irrelevant. Survival was all that mattered. At least others had started to dance by then so I felt less exposed, but the conversation was stilted and the feet were sorely stressed.

Thankfully, supper was announced and, to my surprise, all the men left the hall while the woman gathered round the stove for some heat and a lavish feed. Naively I asked why the men were not having supper too, but was told that they had gone to Murphy's barn to see a match on the box. Sure enough, they returned some time later in great spirits and the whole atmosphere improved dramatically. I later discovered that in that area I should have read the word 'bar' for the word 'box'. Everyone got up on the floor, the musicians excelled themselves, and, since my feet were numb anyway, I ditched the high heels and joined in. We all danced the same steps regardless of tune or rhythm: one, two and clump; one, two and clump . . .

If Miss Lester were in her grave, she would be turning over the whole cemetery.

A 'RELIGIOUS EXPERIENCE'

"Fish or meat? Meat or fish?"

Not that anyone could tell the difference. The steward was obviously still in bad form. His bored tones merged with the monotonous drone of the aircraft's engine. It was only three hours since the last offering and my body clock argued that it was six o'clock in the morning. A suffocating smell of fused fish and meat wafting from the seats behind only emphasised my decision to refuse this delicacy on its fourth appearance.

I squirmed within my allotted twenty-two inches on an unforgettable flight to Japan. 'Down with poverty,' I vowed to myself. 'The next time someone suggests a cut-price, long-haul flight, I will remember every metre of this route. The frequent stops, the disturbingly close-up views of the Indian Ocean and the sparse menu are not worth saving two hundred pence for, let alone the pounds.'

I glanced out at the runway where we had been parked for an hour while waiting to be refuelled, only to see the plane completely surrounded by heavily armed soldiers. The steward assured me they were only protecting us from being hijacked!

Prayer was plentiful on this journey, which was good practice as the purpose of my trip was to attend an interfaith conference on global peace for the liberal-based religions of the world.

I arrived in Tokyo, battered and hungry. The welcome from a host of smiling and flag-waving Japanese was reassuring as I had been anxious about coming to this event alone. I met up with other European representatives and as we were transported to our lodgings I noted that a luxury coach bearing the rather vocal American delegation was pulling up outside a very grand five-star hotel. We travelled on through the city backstreets to a seminary. We were going native, with proper futons on the floor – no westernised mattress for us. We would spend the next two weeks sharing one shelf for suitcase contents, a sheet of greaseproof paper as protection from any snorts and snores from the next room, and a communal bath.

'Pluralism in Religion' was one of the workshop topics, but pluralism in the bathroom did not appeal to me. No showers, but the 'tub' was twelve feet square. No soap or bubbles allowed, women on the hour, men on the half-hour. I could only cope with the dire effects of intense heat and humidity by bathing at four o'clock in the morning when the night revellers were in bed and the dawn worshippers were still asleep. How I cursed my inhibited Irish upbringing in that weary bath at those times.

One of the highlights of the congress was that we were given the opportunity to experience a weekend of some of our host country's religious practices in their own settings. We were divided into various groups and I was invited to join a branch of Shintoism at their retreat house high up in a pine forest on the side of a mountain . . . fortunately accessible by bullet train and coach.

Again the accommodation was traditional Japanese, but in deference to Western ways our hosts had made suitable alterations to their toilet facilities. Knee-high tubular structures of shiny white plastic were loosely placed over the squat holes. Balancing became an exact science as the consequence of the slightest miscalculation was disastrous.

Happily, the Shinto faith encouraged frequent purification rituals throughout the day.

Precisely at dawn, my group was sent to a clearing in the wood that surrounded the temple. The early morning mist was swirling in the sunrays through dew-soaked pine trees with a background orchestra of birdsong, rustling leaves and a solitary bell. We were given brooms of freshly gathered branches to sweep the paths, in total silence, as an 'act of purification'. Faintly, we heard the Shinto priests chanting a haunting continuous single note with the swell rising and falling gently through the trees. Later, when we were invited to join in, we learnt that the continuous sound was produced by each singer taking it in turns to breathe. The words they were singing acted as an aid to meditation. 'One, two, three, four, five, six, seven, eight, nine; one, two, three, four, five, six, seven, eight, nine . . .' over and over again for fifteen minutes before the ceremonies began. The effect was one of overwhelming spirituality.

In an earthier moment I realised that, back home, this might be an ingenious way of persuading reluctant volunteers to clean up the church grounds.

The priests joined us for the breakfast of sticky rice in their full regalia complete with fascinating headgear. Each morning they had arranged for a fully kilted Scottish Presbyterian clergyman to describe the worship of ancestors and nature spirits before they demonstrated their celebratory rituals for weddings, naming ceremonies, and other happy events in people's lives. When I asked how they did the caring, dying and grieving bits, I was told that they left most of that to the Buddhists. Sure enough, in each of the homes I later visited, honourable places were given to both Shinto and Buddhist shrines.

Lunch was usually composed of most artistically arranged set dishes of raw fish accompanied by interesting sauces and more bland, sticky rice. I was such a coward in those days so I ate a lot of seaweed and chrysanthemums with which the cooks had painstakingly garnished their works of art. Having noted the pollution levels of their waterways, I was not keen on tucking into the rest.

For the afternoons, the priests had changed into immaculately tailored city suits and whiter-than-white shirts and they were intent on making everyone thoroughly happy. I politely refused the beer and whisky, but drank several small glasses of a warm liquid before I realised that I was on my seventh glass of sake. Coming on top of my light lunch, things blurred a little, but

I have vague images in my memory of sushi chefs giving a swashbuckling display of flinging cleavers and knives into the air before filleting a whole tuna into slivers. Origami magicians turned coloured papers into what looked like flying elephants and I sobered up in time to watch an ikebana master gazing in rapture at his hour's work on a branch and a flower.

By midnight, it was necessary to become purified once more, this time at a waterfall deep in the forest. A rushing-down-the-mountain waterfall, pouring into a fairy-tale grotto with dozens of bright-green frogs on every ledge – plastic frogs. Dressed in only a cotton kimono with matching scarf round the forehead, I had to stand under that icy, torrential water, head bowed and hands clasped in a gesture of pleading for full purification from the day's dishonourable deeds.

My hands were indeed clasped in fervent prayer, but as my teeth chattered I was yelling, "Aieee! Get me out of here."

Sobriety I had achieved, but I was not too sure if the purification was successful.

Next day, all the delegates met up to exchange experiences. The Rissho Kosei-kai had taken the Dutch and the Indians to deep and meaningful group-therapy Hosa Circles. The Buddhists had taken the French, Swiss and Canadians to feed the poor and tend graves while the Ioten had taken the Americans from their five-star hotel to humble themselves by cleaning out the town toilets. Bless them.

In fairness, they had enjoyed en-suite bathrooms, fixed porcelain toilet bowls, and varied menus. They could even take part in that other Japanese religion, golf, by playing on the course laid out on the rooftop of their hotel, albeit for a fee that would equal my fare home.

Ah! Home. Two full days' journey back to Ireland with the harassed fish-and-meat cabin crew, but then on to a big plate of greasy chips with a crispy, cooked and very dead fish.

THE HOLY EGG

One morning at breakfast time, my husband informed me that we were having a guest to stay for a few days and that she would be arriving in a couple of hours. Nothing daunted – this was a habit of his I had become used to over the years – I rushed to sort out the daughter's room, remove the three dozen cuddly toys, clear the Bon Jovi posters off the ceiling, polish the furniture and make up the bed. All excess items were dumped into the boys' rooms, with their usual cries of protest ignored. I left for work and spent my lunchtime shopping for all those extras needed to make our visitor welcome.

On my return home, there was no sign of our guest as my husband had taken her off somewhere, so I threw some flowers into a jug, arranged them tastefully and put them with drinking water and assorted fruit in her room. Thus the Manse was prepared for a guest, but its incumbent's wife was unprepared for this particular one.

I was introduced to the Rev. Professor Jane Broadbent, head of the Theology Department at William's old university. She was six feet three in height and her width was barely short of anorexic. She wore a full-length grey skirt, black blouse and long grey cardigan reminiscent of a nursery-rhyme witch and carried a heavy black handbag, large enough to hold several naughty children. She proffered a limp, pallid hand to be shaken although I had the distinct feeling that she expected me to genuflect and kiss it.

I learnt that she had travelled here from England on a mercy mission. One of the parishioners had been very keen to enter the ministry and it appeared that her brothers were strongly opposed to the plan. Their protests were not related to the usual concerns about the low pay, women clergy or even doctrinal differences. They were objecting because this exceptionally bright young lady would be leaving the family farm – and as she had not married she was expected to be their domestic slave at the expense of any career of her own. She had written to the college to say that she had given in to their demands, but Miss Broadbent was here to rectify all that. The brothers had reckoned without the ghost of Emmeline Pankhurst.

After the quietest ever family meal, William went to a church meeting and the holy lady stood up from the table and addressed me. "I am going to my room. I will be at prayer from seven to ten. If your husband returns before then he may join me. I will require nothing until the morning, when at eight o'clock I will have breakfast – one boiled egg, one slice of thinly buttered brown toast, orange juice and black coffee. Goodnight!"

It seemed I was relegated to below stairs and obviously not even fit for a one-minute prayer.

I went through the evening's routine with ease as the children had been stunned into obedience about homework and bedtimes. Only the toddler dared to call out for a drink of water. Fear of being invited in to pray for three hours at a stretch was the magic wand that made them disappear from Miss Broadbent's sight and sound. Conveniently, William arrived home after ten o'clock.

Later, when I prepared the breakfast things for the morning, such was the level of tension in the air that I felt utterly devastated when I discovered there was only one egg in the house – and there was a crack in it.

Bear in mind that this happened in the days when local garages sold nothing but petrol and late-night shopping only happened in big cities.

I nipped over the field to beg one from my neighbour.

Unbelievably she had no eggs at all. I phoned my sister. She had just used up her last one.

Somewhat puzzled, she asked, "What is wrong with giving her bacon and sausage instead?"

"You just don't understand," I snapped, now totally beyond reason.

Despair hung heavily over the Manse that night. I had failed my husband and failed the distressed parishioner, all because of one cracked egg. Unable to sleep, I crept downstairs in the dim light of the rising dawn. I stared at that egg. I pictured it oozing into the water. The albumen would stick itself all over the outer shell. The yolk would float off in strings of yellow goo. The shell would be hollow down one side and Miss Broadbent would shower rage and scorn over us all. She would stalk away in disgust and leave the object of her visit to her ruin.

Never had there been such a crisis in the Manse. Problems with head-injured children, alcoholic organists and soggy garden fêtes had been easier to resolve.

Desperation being the mother of invention, I wrapped that wretched egg in six layers of firmly folded tinfoil and positioned it with trembling hands exactly in the centre of a saucepan of cold water. The hob was set at its lowest temperature and I sat on a stool beside the cooker and watched the silver orb lest it rise above a bare simmer – for half an hour.

I gingerly removed the foil without feeling any pain in my scalded fingers – and yes, success was mine. The egg was boiled and the egg was whole!

I cheerfully made up the breakfast tray having dusted off the cut-glass butter dish and ironed the damask napkin. Breakfast in bed for a guest was the only way to cope with the morning rush and surely even Miss Broadbent would enjoy a little spoiling. I knocked on the door of the bedroom and bounced in. "Good morning. It is a lovely day. I thought you would enjoy your breakfast in bed as a treat—"

A funereal voice interrupted me. "I said eight o'clock. It is only five to eight and breakfast in bed is indolence."

Controlling an unholy retort, I plonked the tray on the bed

muttering something about it being here now and closed the door rather firmly, rushed the children out of the house and escaped to my workplace.

Of course, that evening there were lots of eggs on the kitchen table. A dozen from my neighbour, a dozen from William and the ones I had bought myself. Indeed, an egg-less day has never dawned on the Manse since that visit.

Miss Broadbent returned from her mission and it had obviously been a success. I was about to ask how she had resolved the issue when I was silenced by a raised hand as she strode into her room.

"I will have the same breakfast tomorrow, not in my bed and not before eight o'clock. A lightly boiled egg this time. Goodnight. William, you will join me for my three hours of prayer."

I was not sure three hours of penance was enough for what he had put upon me that time!

THE FIRST YEAR

William graduated from theological college after seven long years of study. He knew a lot about higher criticism and ecclesiastical doctrine, but a few months later, when he was installed in a country parish, he realised all that had limited value. What he really needed were the management skills of Richard Branson and the wisdom of Solomon. Sadly, some of his parishioners assumed he had them already.

One wild winter's night, William was wakened out of his sleep by an urgent pounding on the door. Young Jones was standing there, drenched to the skin.

"Ma says you have to come now!" he spluttered between the torrents of water streaming over his face.

"What is wrong, Ricky? Is someone sick? What has happened?"

"Ma says come now!" And he disappeared again into the stormy night.

This happened in the days before William had come to understand the combustion engine so his sole form of transport was a borrowed racing cycle. Living at the back of the Sperrin Mountains, every journey seemed to be up a hill, even when he was coming down one, as he never managed to understand the gears. Widow Jones lived in Trimery on a smallholding close to nowhere, where she eked out a living for herself and four hefty sons who lived in constant terror of her devotion to them. The house was about five miles from the Manse and that night the wind was blowing in every direction except the one towards Trimery. William battled against the freezing force and tried to keep up with the lad. It was two in the morning and his concern about what peril had struck the Jones household was diminished by his doubts as to whether he would even reach it alive.

He staggered into the farmhouse kitchen, sodden and exhausted. Ricky had arrived before him and was steaming in front of the fire. Every lamp in the house was lit and, judging by the assorted nightwear, the rest of the family had been scrambled out of their beds too. William expected the usual welcome of "Sorry we brought you out and would you take a hot cup of tea?" but no such offer came. The atmosphere was as fraught as the weather.

Widow Jones stood red-faced, hair on end, pointing a shaking finger towards the end of the room.

"Here's the minister now. Tell the minister the truth!"

The finger was aimed at Joe. He was sitting apart from his brothers and their wives. His young wife, Sarah, was hunched up on a small milking stool alongside his chair. Joe's cowed head was thrust forward into his hands, his huge shoulders arched over the table and his flame-red hair glowing with the light of the gas lamp beside him. Sarah was staring at the polished flagstones of the floor. Neither looked up. A tense silence filled the room broken only by Widow Jones's angry foot tapping relentlessly.

William looked around the room to find the source of her rage. There was a great heat from a blazing fire in the blackleaded range. Kettle and pans glistened with years of vigorous polishing. The only ornamentation on the rough yellowing walls was an aging sampler stating that 'God is Love' hanging above a rusting tin copy of a shop advertisement that displayed a tailcoated golliwog extolling the virtues of marmalade with the slogan 'Watch out for the Robertson's Golly'.

Joe and Sarah had been married just a few weeks before. It had been a great occasion. Both families had been overjoyed that day. Joe had a good trade, she was working part-time and they had been allocated their council house just that week. What could have gone so wrong?

"Now," the widow shouted, "tell the minister! Out with it! Tell him! He'll get the truth out of ye!"

"Er-hm!" William cleared his throat nervously. "Perhaps I could talk with Joe in the other room," he suggested as it was obvious that Joe was not going to say a word for fear of instant self-incrimination.

"You will not. I want them all to know the truth. Huh! One month wed and three months carrying and now she's trying to say it's our Joe's. That's a lie. No son of mine has shenanigans before the weddin'. They've all been warned often enough that I'd kill 'em. That wee whore has been with another man and is trying to pass it off as our Joe's. Tell the truth now, afore the minister. Whose is it?"

It was clear that murder would have been a lesser sin, but Joe and Sarah were saying nothing. Neither moved a muscle. Everyone else in the room was concentrating on their feet.

William thought it was time to say something illuminating. He stuttered and coughed, but no words of wisdom would come forth. He felt the pressure on him rising, sweat broke out, his legs shook.

"Would you like me to say a prayer?" he offered in desperation, hoping for spiritual guidance for himself as well as for the situation.

"You can pray away if you like," snapped the widow. "It'll do no good now!"

William felt the moment for prayer had just been lost.

Finally, Mrs Jones's patience collapsed. She thumped the table and a gaslight went out in fright. Everyone started up, released from their stupor.

"Right then! Minister or no minister, it's not our Joe's. So it must have been that golliwog from Robertson's jam!"

The walls shuddered as she slammed the door on her way up to bed. William had to hide his rising mirth under a burst of coughing.

On his way down the mountain track in the early morning light he composed a strong letter to his college principal on the inadequacies of the ministerial training courses in relation to family issues.

Six months later he felt somewhat exonerated from his failings on that night. Sarah was safely delivered of a healthy young son, flaunting a thick mop of flame-red hair.

They named him William after the minister and Robert after the golliwog.

A WHITE MUSICAL CHRISTMAS

I was a musical snob. I had become one in my teens due to my enormous efforts to impress 'the spotty boy next door' who had suddenly metamorphosed into a tall, dark, handsome young man with a car of his own and was 'awfully cultured'. I sighed at the sound of his voice quoting Gerard Manley Hopkins, but when it came to music I feigned the most passionate devotion to never-ending string quintets and tone poems just to have my hand held by my Adonis in the cheap student seats. I would have genuinely enjoyed the full orchestral concerts, but the seats cost more for those.

I had gained entrance to university through music as I had only just managed to clear the admission criteria by counting it in as a main subject. At school, pupils were allocated extra credits if they played piano for the morning assembly, so I became quite adept at several hymn tunes. Elvis and the Beatles were wasted on me in those years. I was a devotee to the classics. I too was 'awfully cultured'.

Inevitable disillusionment and a couple of young men later, I married another and went to live in a house with no piano. I was busy trying to prove to the world that I was Superwoman by working full-time, coping with my children and doing all that 'young-married' entertaining. Music was relegated to the local Parish Palladium every Christmas and nursery-rhyme tapes.

Christmas was a time of year that I disliked intensely. The in-laws moved in, the children became hyper, work was frenetic and school Christmas events were squeezed between rehearsals, baking, shopping, cooking and wrapping. Also, I was married to an 'Ulster male', for whom all such activities were solely the responsibility of the woman.

That Christmas Eve I was struggling to manage the usual chaos when I suddenly noticed that we were having a white Christmas. The serene feeling of purity and peace that comes with snow drifting down from a dark velvet sky was just beginning to help me to relax when the phone shattered the scene. It was the church organist phoning from her home in dismay.

"I can't get the car down the lane here," she wailed. "I don't want to let them down. There is a big crowd coming from the hotel for the midnight service as part of their weekend programme. There is no way I am going to make it. Did you not tell me that you play? Would you play tonight?"

The poor woman was in such a state that I assured her that she must not worry any more while thinking to myself that this should not be a problem. I could surely dash off a couple of Christmas carols all right. It was nineteen years since I had touched a piano, but, after all, I had been good enough for school assembly. . . .

There was no time to drive down to the church for a practice as the children still had to be put to bed, the in-laws fed and the turkey stuffed. In fact, I barely made it in time for the service.

I scrambled into the organist's seat, shed my gloves, kicked off my boots and looked around. I had never played an organ in my life and this was an historic instrument that some 100 years ago had been brought over from Windsor Castle. According to the local legend it had once been played by George Frideric Handel himself. It had two manuals and an array of stops that were totally meaningless to me, but hey, George Frideric and I could *handle* this.

I pulled at a couple of the stops and something squeaked so I tried a few others until a deeper sound came forth. Then I set up the music book and prepared to sight-read the chosen carols. Thankfully, there would be no introit.

The minister stepped into the pulpit. It was a large square structure that blocked off sight and sound from the person presiding at the organ. There may have been cleverly arranged mirrors, but as doubt was beginning to replace confidence I saw none of these. I could hear the buzz of a large gathering and I hastily scanned the music for the first carol. Three flats. The first hymn was announced and I started playing.

I could hear my old music teacher's voice in my head: "You are going too fast. Go slower. Keep time. Give people time to get their breath at the end of the lines."

I did. I could not hear the congregation too well, such was my earnest concentration, but that did not seem important. I was discovering that my woefully unexercised fingers did not seem to connect with the keys in the right places. Perspiration made them slide all over the place. No sound corresponded with the notes that were written on the sheet of music before me.

After the first hymn, I removed my coat. The temperature seemed to have risen.

I sensed, rather than heard, the clergyman leaning over the back of his pulpit saying something to me, but as I dared not lift my eyes from the music, nor my hands from the keyboard, I did not hear him. It did seem strange, however, that when I played the next hymn the congregation appeared to have stopped singing some considerable time before I reached the 'Amen'. Shamefully, I was reduced to playing the melody of the last carol with one finger.

Then came those merciful words "Now for the benediction."

One final surge of 'Silent Night' for the final voluntary and it was over. My shoes and gloves were on the floor, my coat was in a heap over the rails and my self-esteem was right at the bottom of my 'awfully cultured' pit.

I reasoned that I would not be seen by anyone if I waited until the church was empty before I extricated myself from the organ seat. I would then slip out the back door, unseen, into the night.

Alas, the snow had covered every inch of the surrounding countryside and my escape was spotted by the local 'fount of all knowledge' from the town.

"Oh, Sheila. I did not see you in church. Wasn't it lovely to see the place so full with all the posh people here from the big hotel? It was such a pity that whoever was playing the organ ruined the whole service by having their Christmas drinkies just a bit too soon, wasn't it? I wonder who was playing tonight? Would you know, dear? I must try to find out."

I fled home, determined to encourage my husband to apply for a job in another part of the country before the identity of this sad musical snob was exposed.

THE EBB AND FLOW OF A PARADISE

The day we had our first burglary was one of the most productive in our family's history.

The thieves had 'cased the joint' well as there was no evidence of ransacking. They had gone straight to the bedside drawer and removed the slim watches and bracelets which we had bought in the madness of youth but which were now useless because of age and girth. Only a small windowpane was smashed.

Fortune prevailed when the insurance man came to assess our losses. He told us we were his first clients. Somewhat overawed by the fact that he had been sent to a manse, he was convinced that such folk would never dispute the figures. The only thing was that other 'burglarees' had warned us that we would never get a fair price unless we doubled our estimates and then agreed half the figure. We compromised and claimed a half extra with such red faces that we were sure he would call the police. To our amazement, and embarrassment, he agreed everything instantly and within a week we were awarded nine hundred pounds.

With such a windfall, tinged with a little guilt, we spent it on a caravan. Holidays had been a financial struggle so this seemed to be the perfect solution. A parishioner said he had a static one going cheap in Ballycastle and we snapped it up eagerly. It was only on the first overnight stay, when I was lying in bed contemplating the ceiling, that I realised that we were not the only crooks in the world. The owner was a civil engineer and yet here I was studying wedges of newspaper stuffed into the roof at irregular intervals with some even aiding an excellent view of the night sky. I awoke cold and wet.

Our suspicions were confirmed when next morning the woman who had the caravan beside us said in astonished tones, “Did you pay money for that? They were going to push it into the sea last week!”

A month later the Ballycastle police telephoned us at home to tell us that the caravan had acquired squatters, a couple of runaway teenagers, so would we like to check for any damage? It was probably a merciful release. We paid for it to be taken away. Crime had not paid in the end.

However, from this experience, we learnt that the location was most valuable in holiday terms, due to its idyllic setting above a small private beach, with a tantalising view of Rathlin Island, an occasional tall sailing ship and, once, even a nuclear submarine.

The added benefit was that our fellow campers were few in number and disliked any notion of being ‘happy campers sharing drinky-poos’ as much as we did. We were all there to escape the city and only wanted to commune with nature and maybe the wee man in the corner shop. Such paradise being in sight, we joined purses with my sister and the bank and purchased a brand-new static caravan – one with electricity, its own loo and a shower. Wow!

We could not wait to move in. My sister and I had agreed to travel up straight after work, hand the money over and wallow in OUR bit of luxury before the families joined us the next day.

Jamie, the site owner, liked to deal in cash only. As I had a busy day ahead, I collected several thousand pounds from the bank early that morning. My work entailed meetings in various city locations, a business lunch and several home visits so I had to ensure that the money was close to me at all times, and secure. I rechecked it every half-hour.

We hared up the road to Ballycastle like Formula One drivers. I unlocked the shiny new door and switched on a light while my sister rushed through to the little bathroom to flush the loo. Children on Christmas morning were less excited. Amused at our lack of sophistication, Jamie came over to collect the payment. He awaited his time, and listened patiently while we chittered on about plans for the flagstone surround, the steps and the garden area. We were fairly subdued when he told us that it would cost us another two hundred pounds for the flagstones.

Eventually the time came to hand over the cash. I took it out from its secure location – in a plastic bag at the top of my knickers. It was still warmish as I handed him the bundle. Well, where else would a woman hide her money when travelling?

Jamie's face was a story in itself. Used to remaining expressionless in North Antrim style, it had quite a struggle not to slacken, but eventually it had to relent. He coughed, spluttered, gasped and then exploded into such hysterical laughter we feared for his hernia. His hand shook as he took the cash.

When he laid the new flagstones for us the next week, he said, quite firmly, that he would not take any money for them after all!

My next visit to the van was on one of those dancing bright blue days when the hills were bursting with golden whin bushes and white horses were galloping along the crests of the navy-blue waves. It was early spring and the longed-for appearance of the sun had brought an unusual number of people out to enjoy a coastal walk. They gathered at the edge of the cliff to watch massive waves pounding the beach. Sitting out on our 'grand terrace' with Jamie, I commented that, although the waves were now raging and hurling themselves downwards with increasing fury, there was no wind blowing on the shore side. It felt surreal.

He explained that the wave phenomenon was brought about by the remnants of a distant hurricane. "Are you worried?" he added.

"Well, I am a bit. If the waves come up any higher they will reach the van. Would that happen?" I asked.

"Sure, why would you be worried? Won't the van float?"

With his face impassive and a glint of a twinkle in his eye, he walked away.

He had turned the tide on me.

A SHEEPISH TALE

Me, driving home from work:

'Weekend at last. Off to the caravan in the morning. Peace for two whole days. Must remember to stop at Tesco's and stock up on the way home. I'll get a steak each, throw in a salad and there's the dinner made. Great. How many will be in tonight? Gerry has a gig, John is out with the girlfriend, and Kevin is staying the night at Owen's. Oops, there's the mobile ringing.'

"Hello, big son! Yes. I'm going up tomorrow. Your Aunt Ruth is on her way tonight. Why? So, what's the problem? You and Owen are coming to Ballycastle too? That's fine as long as you look after yourselves. I intend to do nothing that involves any physical or mental effort. Why? What do you mean it will keep? You have to tell me. I can't wait until tomorrow. What has your aunt got to do with it? Kevin? Hello? Hello?"

'Now what has he done? What could it be that he has to tell me only if Ruth is with me? When that lad is in trouble, he always goes to Ruth first. He confesses to Ruth, she waters it down for me, then I have to sugar the pill for his father. What could it be this time? Hmm. Forget it. I'll just have to wait until tomorrow.'

Me again, next morning in the car: 'For goodness' sake slow down. You didn't see that bicycle at all. Calm down and behave or you'll never get there alive to hear what it is. I am so tired. Couldn't sleep a wink all night. Kevin's voice on the phone kept pounding through my head: “Mum, I have something I have to tell you.”

‘What will I do if that wee girl is pregnant? That must be it. What else would he be so afraid to tell me? His father will kill him. How will I face her mother? She’ll kill him. I’ll kill him.

‘Stop it. He is alive and well. Worse things could happen. Oh no, he is too young to settle down. They’re just not right for each other. Her life will be destroyed too. Didn’t she go for that job in Thailand? How can she raise a child there? Her mother’s in a wheelchair and she hasn’t seen her dad in years. I’ll have to rear it. I couldn’t go all through that again. I am far too old. I’ll have to give up my job. How will we manage? He’ll not have any money for years yet. Two whole families turned upside down because those stupid idiots could not control themselves.

‘Maybe he’s got AIDS. How would he know her history? She could say anything and he would believe her! How would we find out? I could get a test done on him at the hospital on Monday. I’ll phone George. He would rush it through for me. Don’t start panicking until you know for certain. Still, he hasn’t been eating too well. What are the symptoms? Lumps and pneumonia. Did he have a cough? I could nurse him at home. There’s room for a bed downstairs and Ruth would help, but he is too young. I’ll never get mad at him again. Just let him live. Please, Lord, let him live.

‘Have to pull myself together. Can’t see the road through these tears. There’s Ruth’s car at the van and the lads have already arrived. Please, please, let him be all right.

‘Be cool now. He will be very distressed, as he’s bottled this up for ages. If he is ill you don’t want to frighten him. Be understanding, not judgemental. Look at him. I am sure that’s torment behind those eyes. Owen is looking very silent.

‘Here we are. All seated in a row. Ruth is throwing warning looks at me. He must have told her already. Listen. What’s he saying?’

“Mum, Owen and I have something to tell you.”

‘Ah! He’s gay. I never noticed before. Phew! That’s OK. I

can live with that. But why is he taking his shoes off now? Just shut up and listen.'

"Owen hasn't told his parents yet either. Look, I am eighteen now and I'm tired of deceiving you and always having to walk around the house in my socks. . . ."

'Socks? What is he getting at? Then it's not the girl. You don't get AIDS on your feet. Then what?'

"We've had a tattoo done on our ankles."

'A tattoo? Is that what all this is about? Ah, thank you, Lord.'

"I knew you would disapprove so it is only a little one and you can only see it if I am in my bare feet. . . . See there? It's a wee sheep. He's called Shadwell and Owen's is called Meryl. Ende has one too, but his is holding a pint and he is called Wayne. Please don't be angry."

Angry? I can hardly speak under overwhelming waves of relief and laughter.

As we share a big hug together, he is saying, "You know, I am quite hurt. I have been sick with worry about telling you and all you do is laugh. Why have you taken this so well?"

"Son, dearest, if you only knew. . . ."

THE CLERGY LINE

Alastair dodged out of the way as his father charged through the kitchen doorway, clutching a scarlet tulip in one hand and a piece of orange Lurex material in the other.

"You know," he said, "other boys' dads go about their houses with a spanner or a plank in their hands. Ours has a flower in his. It's bad enough being a clergy son, but a flower arranger's son too! What chance have I got for some street cred around here?"

He fled in case he had to help his father to condition his foliage. In the silence that followed, I remembered a time when I too was not happy about being related to the clergy. In fact, I am fourth in a line of clergy. Great-uncle, grandfather, father, and then I married one.

Working in the hospital, I had been asked to see an elderly man who had a neurological disease. He had become so withdrawn that it was difficult for the doctors to work out if he was *unable* to speak or just *unwilling* to speak. I checked his notes before I went into the ward and noted that this Mr White was almost ninety years old and came from the village of Raloo.

I knew this place. It was a tiny village deep in the heart of the Antrim Hills where my dour and stern grandfather had ministered while his sons, unbeknownst to him, entertained the locals with piano and fiddle as part of the local ceilidh band. I reckoned I knew enough about Raloo to help raise an interest from Mr White and so test out his ability to communicate.

I sat down beside his bed and introduced myself, speaking clearly and distinctly in case he was a bit deaf. No response. I asked how he liked the ward, the food, the staff and the doctors. He stared ahead, motionless. I tried for any complaints, worries or anxieties. Nothing. Then I played my trump card: "I see you come from Raloo. Not many people come from there, do they? Actually, my father came from your part of the world. He was brought up there in the nineteen twenties. Would you have been living there then?"

A flicker of interest appeared at last. He turned his face towards me, leaning closer as if to study for any family likeness.

'Yippee,' I thought, 'I'm through. Thank you, Gramps.'

Mr White spoke hesitatingly and formed each word with great difficulty: "What's the name?" he asked.

Pleased at this progress, and with a certain amount of pride creeping into my voice, I said, "McCleery. My grandfather was the Rev. John McCleery. I'm a daughter of his son John, who also became a clergyman in . . ."

I tailed off as Mr White jerked bolt upright, made a rasping sound in the back of his throat and hurled from it the largest lump of spit that I have ever had the fortune to duck. It landed with considerable force on the medical chart at the end of his bed. He then swore, very loudly and very clearly, before adding, "Curse the man! That so and so bought up our only pub, kept the licence and then turned it into a flaming temperance hall. That man was the ruin of Raloo!"

Somewhat dismayed at this turn of events, I tried again: "Isn't there a place that used to be called McCleery's pub in the townland?"

"Ach! That was the village pump he put in at the cross and that was the only drink for ten miles round after he'd done his work! Now gerrawayaff. I want no truck with anyone of that family round me." He paused and eyed me thoughtfully. "Unless you would see your way to righting McCleery's wrong and fetch a pint of stout in here?"

The ward sister greeted me at the door.

"Well, how did you get on with Mr White? I think the disease must have reached his vocal chords now. Did you get anything out of him at all?"

"Sister," I replied, "I can assure you that I got more than talk out of that man this day. His speech is perfect."

"How did you do it?"

"Now, that is a secret that only comes with *my* family's genes. But a bottle of stout would keep him talking the best for now."

OH, TO BE GRANDPARENTS BEFORE WE ARE PARENTS!

I read a quote the other day that struck home: 'Few things are more satisfying than seeing your children have teenagers of their own.' I thought of my forty-something son. So kind and thoughtful, you could take him anywhere and he would rise to any occasion. But, there was a time . . .

Most mothers will be familiar with the scene. The once handsome son suddenly becomes unwashed, permanently dressed in the holeyest jeans and the hair lies lank, below the shoulders. The magnified music pounding his ears renders him incapable of speech so conversation is confined to toneless grunts. As for essential deep and meaningful discussions about his career, forget it!

In those days, I was unaware that below that laid-back exterior was a wee fella trying to make sense of the big mad world and terrified of what might be ahead of him. Added to this state of confusion, his hormones were running amok. It was years before I heard about some of the trials he had suffered in his efforts to be 'cool' during that period.

Having attended an all-boys school he was sixteen before he noticed girls. One particular lassie came into view that he fancied madly. He even walked a mile from school just to board the bus outside her college. He never actually spoke to her, but just yearned and sighed from afar. He thought it would look cool if he leant nonchalantly against the hedge a few yards away from where she chatted with her friends. What he did not see was that the hedge was composed of thin wild briars. He realised his mistake when he collapsed with maximum indignity, and a suppressed yelp, right through the hedge. The girls laughed mercilessly. In desperation, he decided to spring back up as though that was what he had intended to do, only to find himself totally grounded by the briars, as firmly as the little people had tied down Gulliver.

He changed tack while actually dating the next girl. Thinking it would be romantic to serenade her from below her bedroom window, he crept into her garden, guitar in hand. In the darkness he could only find edging stones around the grass so he fired one or two up at the window. Of course it shattered. Our frustrated troubadour rapidly disappeared into the night. Sure he had got away with it, he was horrified later in the week when the mother greeted him at the door with a glint of amusement in her eye. Wordlessly she handed him a receipt for the replacement costs of a large plate-glass window. Ten years later she became his mother-in-law and I only heard that story on his wedding day!

Yesterday he called into the family home.

"I'm awfully worried about Lucy. She won't revise and she wears the most indecent clothes and she won't talk to me any more and that boy next door is always looking at her . . . and . . . and . . ."

My first instinct was to punch the air with a shout of "Yes!" but my mother's instinct stepped in. I made him a cup of tea.

"Sit down, son. We need to talk. Do you remember . . . ?"

TERRORS OF THE NIGHT

I woke up as usual, one full minute before the baby demanded his four a.m. feed. I lay there in the stillness of the night savouring the moment of quiet, waiting for my cue. It arrived on time. The snuffle, the gentle searching cry followed by the wail of hunger. Resisting the urge to waken the contented, snoring form on the other side of the bed, I padded downstairs to heat the bottle.

Living beside the main Belfast–Dublin railway line was always eventful, especially as one of the main road crossings was at end of our driveway. Noise was never a problem; silence came only when trains were not running because of a breakdown or, more often in those days, a bomb scare. As children, we saw the last steam engines, the first new Dublin Enterprise, and learnt to count by the number of wagons passing by on the long freight trains. Now, as parents, we could time the children's departure for school by the whistle of the eight twenty-five, and the signalmen who manned the crossing were excellent watchdogs for the house when we were away on holiday.

A week earlier there had been great excitement because a magnificent modern signal cabin had been officially opened. The local dignitaries had attended and a speech was made about its strength and technology with particular reference to the unfortunate demise of its wooden predecessor. This had been brought about two years earlier by a paramilitary group who had feared that it was a major threat to their security. Indeed, such was the extent of this concern that within a few hours of the 'grand opening' they blew up the new one as well!

With baby settled back to sleep, I was pondering on the futility of these happenings on my way back to bed. As I started across the hallway, I noticed car lights approaching the sealed-off gates of the crossing. Three clearly silhouetted figures climbed over the gates, each in a sinister crouching position, obviously up to no good. In one swift burst of community spirit, I dashed into the kitchen, switched on the light and dialled the number for the police station.

"There is something very suspicious going on at the railway crossing. Three men are putting a bomb on the tracks." A little overdramatic, perhaps, but it had been one of those days.

"Yes, madam. Now, what is your name? And how do you spell that? And what is your address? Are you living alone? Give me your phone number and I will call you back after I have spoken to the inspector. . . ."

I knew they thought I was a complete idiot, but I was sure they would thank me one day.

An awful thought struck me. I had put the light on. The evildoers would have seen it and they would reckon that I had called the police. They would ambush the police and shoot us as witnesses . . . and . . . and . . . I froze in panic.

A few minutes later, my fears were confirmed. The car lights turned and were very slowly edging their way up the driveway. My thought processes went into overdrive. 'What should I do? If I go back upstairs, they will see me cross the hall; if I wake my husband and children, we could climb out the back window and head over the field to our neighbour. But is there time for that? If I wake them up, they will be terrified. Perhaps, if I let them sleep, they will die in their sleep and won't feel anything.' The lights stopped moving. I could hear the clunk of a car door. I thought the pounding in my head would wake up the whole household now. 'They must be circling the house. This is it. Who will find our bodies in the morning? Oh, my hair rollers! Must get them out as they will look most undignified in the forensic photographs.'

And so I did! I actually stopped to take them out and brush

my hair into shape. Only then did I call the police station again.

“Please come at once. They have surrounded the house. They are coming in to kill my children. Please help!” I screamed hysterically down the phone.

“Madam,” came a calm reply, “we radioed a car in your area. That was a police car at your gate. The men were chasing a car thief who had abandoned his vehicle at the crossing gates. The men in your driveway are those policemen. They have just reported in to say that all is well. Goodnight.”

I slunk back into bed.

“What is all the noise about? Baby all right?” grunted my husband.

“Well, I was chasing some terrorists away who were coming in to kill us all, and . . .”

“Oh? Good. ’Night, dear.”

A NIGHTMARE IN THE NORTHERN IRELAND EIGHTIES

This is worse than a night terror. A sodden winter night, roads deserted except for the army patrols and an occasional half-lit taxi. I am searching, searching, these ghoulish streets, through torrential rain and blinding tears, for my seventeen-year-old son.

The evening had been frenetic. The younger children were doing homework while I tried to supervise them between washing dishes and making yet another loaf of sandwiches. The concert in the church hall next door was scheduled to begin at eight. Boilers had to be switched on, and chairs set out. The doorbell never paused as the performers' demands became endless. One needed a cushion, another wanted a scarf. Someone said there wasn't enough light and where could they lock up their handbags? What time was supper and when were the floral bouquets coming? Then Dad needed a clean shirt ironed and did I know who last had the microphone?

Somewhere in the midst of the melee I heard my son saying he was going into Belfast, but I had no time to listen to the where and with whom.

This lapse is haunting me now. As I drive I ransack my memory in an attempt to recall anything he had said that might lead me to find him. I should have been listening instead of allowing myself to become so frazzled.

I slam on the brakes. There is something on the side of the path. I slosh through the puddles to reach it, hoping and dreading, but it's just a heap of junk covered with tarpaulin.

At midnight, I had eased into the chair with aching feet and choral overkill. About two seconds later I realised that the last bus would have been in long ago, and the son was not. At first I reckoned he would get a taxi or, if all else failed, phone home apologetically looking for a lift. An hour went by. Nothing. My husband said I was worrying too much and went to bed. That awful, gut-wrenching sick feeling took hold and icy claws tore through my insides. My first thought was that he had missed the bus, had started to walk home, had taken a lift from total strangers who turned out to be members of one of the paramilitary gangs who delighted in torturing and murdering random young men. In my milder scenarios he had been run over and lay unnoticed in the ditch, he had been hit on the head and did not know who or where he was . . .

I stop the car again. The road ahead has become impassable because of my uncontrollable sobbing as the mental images of my fears take hold.

I had phoned every one of his friends. All parents understood about middle-of-the-night calls then because of the tragic times we were living in, but no one had seen him. One remembered he had mentioned a new girlfriend. He even remembered her surname and that she lived in South Belfast with her granny. I knew of a street directory in my workplace that listed all the residents of Belfast, but the office would be locked up. Despair drove me to the police station. The duty officer listened patiently. Attempting to reassure this neurotic mother, he suggested it was too early to panic and that all young lads skived occasionally.

"Not mine!" I shouted as more tears flowed. "If you won't do anything, let me at least have your street directory."

"We haven't got one," he replied.

I did not believe him and left the station in a helpless rage.

William had finally risen from his dead sleep and joined in the action. I was into my organising mode. Together we phoned all the hospitals.

"We're not allowed to give out that information under data protection" was every response.

I contacted a work colleague, a ward sister who was still on duty that night. She phoned back.

"No one of that name or description brought in anywhere last night, and, Sheila, I checked the city morgue too. He's not there."

A neighbour came and took charge of our younger, frightened children. Dad, already sunk into deep grief, was unable to speak. At that stage, I took off in the car to search the streets, any streets, and here I am now.

I cannot bear the waiting. All I can see is the body wrapped in a bin liner. Feeling the sheer terror of the last hours of his life, and groaning with the pain of it, I drive furiously, relentlessly nowhere. Dawn grudgingly appears. I turn home hoping he has made contact, but only a hollow nothingness meets me.

From these depths, I strangely remember I had been phoning a client yesterday and she lives in the girlfriend's district. I look up my work diary. Her number begins with 9076. Searching the directory for the girl's surname, I call all similar names whose number starts with 9076. At the seventh one, I get Granny. Her granddaughter says she has been with my son, but last saw him at the taxi rank. She seems unconcerned. I am destroyed by the dead end.

With nothing left to 'organise' I flee round to the empty church and fall on my knees screaming at God to bring him home to me. My sister runs in after me half an hour later.

"He's phoned. He's all right. He's on his way home!"

"Where is he? What happened? Is he hurt?"

"I was so excited to hear him," she replies, "I forgot to ask, but he is OK and he is on his way."

The next hour is all of eternity, relief and angst. I am rooted to the front step until he appears, walking slowly, head bowed.

I fly down the driveway and hug him so hard that we both fall to the ground. William follows, sobbing and shaking, and together we just hold each other until his siblings have to tear us apart with cries of "Let him breathe! It's our turn!"

My son sits in the kitchen just repeating that he is sorry. Questions can come later. He is home and safe. Exhausted, he heads for bed. My sister follows to check him over with her nursing skills, before he falls into a deep sleep.

"Psst! Outside." Sisters really are mothers' best friends.

"I got the story, but for heaven's sake, never say I told you this or he will never trust me again, and don't dare tell his father. The two of them had a meal and then sneaked back to the house as Granny was out. They were doing what they shouldn't when Granny returned unexpectedly, so he hid under the bed. The plan was to escape once Granny fell asleep. Only she was a heavy woman and her bed sagged to the floor. He was trapped. There he lay, scared stiff – as well he might be – until she went out next morning to the shops. When you phoned the house, 'yer woman' was too afraid of Granny's temper to say where he was. Once freed, he phoned home, knowing all hell was already loose. He feels even worse now because of the reception he got instead of a fierce scene and six months' grounding, not to mention excommunication. I think he will punish himself all right."

They say it is an ill wind . . . and it is true. I was the fortunate one after all. After witnessing that nightmare, not one of our children dared to dream of being late home again.

A BLIND PANIC

"We are having lunch out today," said Liz to the seven young men. "Claire and I will take you to the Duck and Drake, where the food is good and it's not too crowded. We'll leave here at twelve. Three will go with Claire and the rest with me as I have Dad's car today. OK?"

It was the culmination of the eight-week rehabilitation course. Lunch in a pub was an experience these young men had not enjoyed since losing their sight. They were going to try out their newly acquired mobility skills. They still felt self-conscious, but venturing out in a group of like-afflicted people would boost their courage and hide their embarrassment.

Claire had been quite nervous when she met this group – her first since qualifying a few months earlier. They were big lads, all in their twenties, and according to their files two had been joyriders, three had done time for assault and the other two were public-school graduates. The only thing they had in common was their blindness, which had developed within the last year as a result of a genetic condition. They had either total black blindness or light perception only.

They were a tough bunch initially and tried so hard to be cool and macho, but underneath they were terrified, depressed and angry. As the weeks progressed they formed a strong bond. Claire soon found them to be kind, caring individuals who belied their outward image of tattooed knuckles, hoodies and untempered language. Sharing their experiences of blindness also led to swapping other useful life skills. The posh pair learnt how to milk the benefits system, the ex-cons learnt how to play guitar and the former car thieves were fast becoming computer nerds.

Liz had suggested the Duck and Drake as it was quiet and had easy parking and plenty of room between tables to move around without bumping into other customers. The boys had to make their own way in, find seats and order their own food and drink without any help from their tutors.

The plan went well. It was a great success and Claire could see their confidence soaring. She was very proud of them . . . and of herself.

"Would you go on while I go to the loo?" said Liz as they prepared to leave. "Just leave my folk at the car," she added.

Claire remembered that Liz had brought her dad's Honda today and she spotted it on the far side. She told the lads to wait beside it and then put the others into her own car.

A smart-suited salesman came out of the pub, talking loudly on his mobile phone. He was struggling with order forms clutched under one arm while trying to hold his phone as his briefcase and car keys were in the other hand. Claire was just settling into her seat when she saw the Honda's lights flashing in response to the salesman's clicker. The four young men, having heard the clunk of the locks being released, scrambled into the vehicle.

She had left them at the wrong Honda!

The startled salesman, seeing four hefty, tattooed men in hoods taking over his property, dropped his papers and hollered into his phone, "Hijack! Hijack! Get the police!"

The wind whipped his papers out of his hands and he stood transfixed, unsure whether to go for his orders or his car first.

"Oh no, no!" Claire cried out, pounding her head on her steering wheel.

"What's wrong? What is it?" Her unseeing passengers became alarmed in their darkness as they didn't know what to do to help her.

She cringed into her seat. "I'm OK. Stay put. I'll see you home now."

Across the car park, the four suspected hijackers were tumbling over themselves trying to get out of the car again, shouting, "Where is it? What's going on, pal? Someone hijacking your car, mate? Leave this to us. We'll sort him out! Where are you?" They took off in all directions trying to follow the sound of the owner's voice, determined to halt this heinous crime!

Claire's little Suzuki Jeep gave her a panoramic view. She saw the bar staff charging out the door to see what was happening. She saw the salesman running wildly away from his approaching helpers, his papers littering the whole car park. She saw the flashing blue light of the approaching police car and she saw Liz marching furiously towards her. There was only one thing to do.

She put her car into gear and fled.

A CLOVEN CLOUT

Oh, mean and horned beastie, you dare to stand and graze
So wrapped in peace, munching cud, unwary of a world
Fighting pestilence, famine, war or trials.
Heart's-ease surrounds your endless furrowing for the sweet grass
So newly sprung from winter's slumber.

You were born into this paradise to ease the toil of man,
To consume wild grass that he must cut and bend and mow.
To please you both with good intention, a deal, secure and fair.
The meadow shared as nature sought, by man and beast united.
No one thought of harboured vengeance.

What evil then possessed you? Which deft imp pervaded
Your soul, altered your ego and swiftly dealt that blow
On me, mere five years old, so many springs ago? I ne'er forget the day
I frolicked mid daisies, celandine and moss, gathering twigs for kindling
To bring glow and warmth to evening hearth.

Suddenly, silently, you scooped me up and skyward flung
My doll-like frame, clearing clouds, scattering birds in flight.
Returning, airless, through space, to land on painful tufts of ground.
I heard distant, tearful screams of fright and felt world pain and woe,
Not knowing whence, how, they came from me.

Noontide stilled, shock absorbed, compassion healed the wounds.
I peeked for pitiless weapon that had rough-smote my day.
There you stood, head bowed, serenely ruminating on green shoots,
Deaf to terrified tears, parental protests, global gloom, but glowering.
"Nothing to do with me." Oh, goat of guile.

PARIS BEFORE FEMINISM

Purple feet will always remind me of my first visit abroad.

The school trip was my idea of anticipatory heaven. It had taken months to persuade my parents that they could afford it, and they finally allowed me to join the fourth form's adventure to Paris.

Our guardians were the headmistress and her deputy and they were determined that this trip would be educational and not a 'jolly spree'. They devoted themselves to showing us everything we ought to see, not what we wanted to see – for which, in hindsight, I have been very grateful as subsequent visits to that great city have generally been dominated more by Disneyland than the Louvre.

We were route-marched along French pavements, pausing on Alexander III's bridge over the Seine for detailed history lectures on '*Les Ponts du Seine*'. Coached to Chartres Cathedral, the Palace of Versailles and on to the village of Fontainebleau, we saw where the first Impressionists painted the cupboard doors of their local tavern in payment for food during their years of obscurity. We boated along the Seine in the evening, enjoying the sights when searchlights shone on the clinched courting couples along the romantic Left Bank. The Arc de Triomphe, the Eiffel Tower and even 365 stone steps were climbed to study gargoyles on the roof of Notre Dame. Then there was more trudging up the Champs-Élysées, meditating in the Louvre and posing on the steps of Montmartre. The litany of sights was alleviated by a daily remission at a pavement cafe for a *citron presse* – ah, such nectar and on one dramatic occasion when the head had her handbag stolen inside Notre Dame, of all places.

From day one, the squeezing commenced. On the Metro, seats were strictly limited so we found ourselves standing very close to men whose consumption of garlic utterly overwhelmed our senses and whose hands seemed to ceaselessly squeeze our embarrassed bottoms.

All this cultural exercise was exhausting. On hearing us moaning about the sore feet one evening, the head gave us some tiny crystals of potassium permanganate, nicked from the school lab. We were to bathe our feet in warm water sprinkled with one or two crystals and so harden our feet and soothe the pain.

Bliss! I suffered from pes planus – that is, very flat feet. Indeed I had once been subjected to having them 'electrocuted' in wooden boxes of water by some insane medic. During our treks throughout Paris I had been nicknamed the Cow's Tail by the headmistress, due to my ability to always be hobbling last in line, so I reckoned these magic crystals would end my pain and my humiliation.

I did not sprinkle. I gathered up every grain of crystal I could find and added the lot to my footbath. Next morning the sheets were purple, the floors were purple and my feet were deep, deep purple, right up to my knees.

The pain did not abate much, but I had no more Frenchmen cosying up to squeeze *my* bottom for the rest of that trip.

A TITANIC PERSONALITY

Elizabeth Law Barbour Andrews considered her name so unsuitable that at the age of four she persuaded her relatives to call her by the initials and thus established her individuality. As her mother grieved, and in due course remarried, Elba was somewhat sidelined to the extent that she lived in her own world without the pressures of conventional society of the day. She told me once that she hated school holidays as she was invariably sent to 'various relatives who felt obliged to be kindly towards her', as she put it. Her Mother, Helen, was the youngest daughter of the Barbours of Conway, Dunmurry, a familiar name in the linen industry of Ulster, as was her father's family in Comber, County Down.

She exuded generosity and had a personality to match her untempered body. On that first visit to the Manse, she noticed that the new building was set in half an acre of mud and immediately offered to bring ground-cover plants from around her cottage. She arrived next day in her other car, a tiny Fiat. Inside, packed to the roof, were mounds of earth with vivid orange-and-green montbretia along with the resident worms and beetles.

"Out of my way. I will plant these. Wouldn't do for a clergyman to be seen wallowing in mud like a hippopotamus."

In the pouring rain, with her wellington boots and voluminous tweed cape, she waded into the task, arms working away and feet slithering everywhere.

"Good morning, my man. Will you tell your father that a descendant of Henry Montgomery is here to see him?"

David dutifully repeated this message to his father, but in awestruck tones. Aged five, he did not quite understand this sixty-year-old woman of rather large proportions, dressed in flowing robes topped with layers of silken scarves in clashing colours.

"I am a descendant of Henry, who lives in your graveyard, and I believe I am your parishioner now that I have moved into this area," she boomed as she took over our hallway. She turned to David again. "You look like an intelligent boy. Go and look at my car and tell me what it is."

Accustomed to being shooed out of the way when his father had visitors, David reluctantly wandered outside but came rushing back shouting, "It's a boat! It's a boat! It has a propeller!"

"Well done," said Henry's great-great-niece. "And I am the only person left in Ireland who has a licence to drive it on the River Liffey, which is not much use to me but I insist on doing it just because I can."

This lively caller was Elba Andrews, born in 1910 and tragically orphaned only two years later when her young father, Thomas Andrews, chief designer for Belfast's Harland & Wolff shipyard, became perhaps the most tragic figure that went down with the *Titanic* on April 15th 1912.

Elba loved all things natural and, to my particular delight, on days when she was on flower duty for the church she would arrive at morning service, two verses into the first hymn, bearing a bucket stuffed full of fresh wild bluebells amid a mass of cow parsley, still sparkling with the morning dew. The impact was greater than many a sermon.

Being a bit of a loner, she travelled extensively and her holidays were always timed to avoid the 'Do come to us this Christmas' offers which she had dreaded most of her life. She went overland as she distrusted flying and often took her bicycle with her. On her return she would very kindly agree to give a talk to the congregation in language that invoked vibrant and dramatic images. Her description of 'almost attending' the Shah of Persia's birthday party produced a vision that outdid the detailing of the glamorous grandeur of the occasion. She arrived at the gates of the Great Palace on her bicycle, after riding for miles through desert sands, just to have a sneak view of all the glamour and dignitaries.

In Istanbul she went to an ancient Turkish bath to cleanse her pores from the dust and sweat of the roads. It was a communal arrangement, tiered like a wedding cake, and the ladies laid themselves out on the marble layers submitting their ample, scantily towelled forms to the steam and the heat. Elba was allocated a place at the top, but was a little overcome, she said, "not by the heat but by the sight of the larger ladies whose stomachs flowed down between their legs onto the tier below".

Her last adventure, in the early seventies, took her to a remote village in India. Exhausted after cycling for days, she went to bed early but was roused by the sound of shouting outside her window. A villager's house was alight. A prosperous neighbour had a swimming pool and the locals needed to use its water to prevent the fire from spreading along the street. Voices became louder and gunfire broke out when the man refused access to his precious commodity. As Elba lay there, listening to the sounds of rioting and the smell of gunfire and burning, she felt quite homesick for her Belfast home.

One day she called to say that she had been offered a job and so would be away for some weeks. She was to make an inventory of the artefacts of the Guinness family's stately home in County Sligo. She would be living in for several weeks and was eagerly looking forward to the task.

The call came two days later. Like her father's, Elba Andrews's departure from this world was premature and tragic. An overloaded lorry ploughed into her little Fiat on a twisting lane near the stately home.

Her death created a chasm that has never been filled, but her personality has left an unforgettable imprint on the lives of those who are privileged to have known her, however briefly.

HEIGH-HO, THE WEED (WITH APOLOGIES TO GERALD MANLEY HOPKINS)

I have an affinity with nature. I love to see its most natural state where everything is free to make its own choices about where and when to be – or not.

Take my pot plants – please take my pot plants. Within a week of being tended, watered and fed, they drop their heads and wilt. They do not appreciate my ministrations and prefer to die rather than suffer. Even a thirty-year-old bonsai tree committed suicide within a month of moving in.

I feel more at peace in an ancient wood, crafted by nature with bluebells and wild anemones than in any meticulously designed formal parterre standing to attention, as in Versailles (with apologies to all those talented and industrious horticulturists).

When not 'raptured' in a wooded glen I study the flora in my lawn. Like the chicken's egg, its myriad properties never cease to amaze me.

My husband cuts the grass occasionally, thus eliminating the most toil-free and practical piece of nature this side of the equator: the *Taraxacum officinale*, harbinger of summer, supermarket of our ancestors, the dandelion.

It arrived 30 million years ago without causing a single death or injury to any adventurous plant hunter, unlike the Douglas fir that grows nearby. Resistant to blight and bugs, and me, it appears in copious quantities on my grass every year. I *feel* spring when I behold its cheerful yellow head standing proud. Yet I did not have to spend cold hours in a greenhouse, planting, pricking out, propagating and pruning.

Many consider the dandelion a weed, yet it has attributes that would reduce our household bills substantially if only we had listened to our forefathers. Fresh young leaves bring a tangy taste to a salad and the golden petals can be coaxed into a light white wine. Dandelion tea is used today as a diuretic and a tonic for the blood, but who remembers that the roots also produce a decaf coffee when they are toasted, ground and boiled?

And there's more.

Inside those roots and mature leaves vital minerals and vitamins abound along with medication for so many bodily dysfunctions that the plant could open up a pharmacy in itself. A Chinese herbalist using crushed, boiled, chopped, mashed, roasted, dried or fermented dandelion will find an answer to most gastric-related discomforts. Almost unbelievably, he will also find a way to ease the outside bits too, for that saintly plant can even be made into an ointment that will cure piles.

With the exception of the disdainful horse, most grazing animals know about the benefits of dandelions. Honeybees seek out its reliable pollen to appease the demands of their queen.

And there is magic too, for every child knows how to find out what time it is just by blowing on a dandelion clock. And sure, by blowing all the seedlings off in one go their wishes will come true.

When one recalls the tulip mania of the seventeenth century, when fortunes were lost or found on the price of one tulip bulb, what price should a few dandelions fetch now?

Mother Nature, thank you.

THE TREE FOR ALL SEASONS

"Ouch! Not again. Stop! You're too old for tantrums, Missy. What is it this time?"

Limey winced as Missy vented her latest frustration on her favourite tree. Limey's proper name was *Tilia cordata.* Proud of his nickname, 'The Lovers' Tree', he reckoned he deserved it with his shapely form, delicate lime blossom and heart-shaped leaves. He was the tallest tree in the garden and over 100 years old, but had lost count of his age after layers of bird droppings and smudge had hidden his birthday rings.

He enjoyed looking after the family in the big house. It had been fun to watch the little ones playing below and he smiled to see them chase his seeded bracts when they floated off in the sunshine like fairy helicopters. He helped the children to climb up high into his strong branches and took care to keep them safe. His roots became a playhouse for the girls, and boys used his trunk for target practice. Oldies seldom came up to that part of the garden, so he was their deputy. It was to Limey each child came to play, to hide, to whisper secrets, to meet and to weep. As they grew, he was hugged for joy when things went right and he was drenched with tears when they didn't. Their kicks of frustration and rage never really hurt him, but always he had just the right way to calm them down. He remained strong, silent and loyal.

The devotion was mutual.

One day a stranger came and tramped all over the neighbourhood. He measured and paced about. He stared hard at Limey and measured some more. Loud phone discussions revealed that there was to be a new development nearby and Limey stood directly in the path of the access road.

He would have to die.

The parents visited the tree and shook their heads, wondering how the young folk would take the news. They knew that Limey had been a tower of strength to them all. The youngest son, out in Australia, was the first to be told. When the other children heard they were completely blown away, that their protector was to be cut down in the prime of his life.

Limey shivered at the rising storm.

Early on the day of execution, Limey heard the lorry. He stiffened and tried to stand tall, but his leaves curled and shrivelled in the gale that the storm had brought on. He saw a taxi arrive and was surprised to see the youngest lad had returned home. Then a minibus appeared, packed with school friends.

Limey watched anxiously when suddenly everyone poured out of the house and rushed towards him. Each person was carrying a chain. The wind howled. He could no longer control his shaking.

Led by the lad from Oz, all the children and their friends scrambled up among Limey's broad branches and padlocked themselves onto him. The tree-killers dared not raise a saw.

It took two weeks and 100 hours of argument before the storm abated and the power of youth prevailed.

With that memory forever engraved into his soul, Limey leant down to the frantic teenager below.

"Come close, Missy. You need a big tree hug."

THAT FARAWAY PLACE

As I sit on the verandah in my nightdress at six o'clock in the morning, I feel I am in paradise. The sky is a brilliant blue and it is going to be hot again. Cockatoos and whipbirds own this time and the sparrows are hopping all over the table looking for an easy breakfast.

It is jet lag that has me up so early, appreciating the sights, sounds and smells of this place before the action begins. The roar of the surf at the bottom of the hill summons the young folk to tumble out of their assorted camper vans parked above the miles of glistening beach while, high up behind, the hang-gliders launch themselves off the lighthouse cliffs to catch the soaring thermals before they go to work.

A door slides open and the familiar whiff of sweat and smoke announces the arrival of my hung-over son as he slides onto the bench beside me. I am trying to think of some last-minute motherly wisdom to impart to him, but his phone rings at the same time as the door buzzer sounds. One is the bride-to-be and the other is the still-inebriated photographer. He has lost his camera and she is wailing that she has forgotten to collect the basket of rose petals.

On the flight over I was sad and fearful about this wedding of my youngest child to some foreigner in such a faraway land. Gradually I'm moving on to more selfish thoughts of being able to return time and time again to this Eden. I have decided that their union is perfect. Indeed, I have fallen totally in love with this place, its lifestyle, its warmth and its people.

The village has one main street with a pub (or hotel, to the villagers) at one end beside the beach, and the foothills of the rainforest at the other. No 'Big Mac' or 'K.F.C.' signs spoil the rows of gaily coloured stalls and cafés that spill onto the shady boardwalks. Barefooted strangers of every age and hue greet each other at the veggie-juice bars and discuss the evils of war or the shrinking planet with the checkout girl at Woolworth's – the only place to find a blast of air conditioning or something for tea. The Global Gossip Internet Café is filled with backpackers emailing their parents back home: 'Send more money. We're staying on here!' It is impossible to find employment even as a binman or ice-cream vendor without having a double honours or a PhD, such is the competition among those on whom this place has cast its spell.

It is the de-stressing zone of Australia. Six pages of the local newspaper are filled with advertisements for every imaginable therapy, treatment, ideology and service, from the Institute of Vibrating Medicine to Floating Stones through to the Crystal Palace Experience. Nature is thoroughly conserved and wildlife roams free. The rich and the poor flock here in search of the cure-all despite the fine cottage hospital, although it is utilised well enough by the more traditional residents. Overall there is an intoxicating atmosphere of world cultures blending into peace and harmony – possibly heightened to some extent by the recreational smokers and local brews.

I am roused from these ponderings by the rest of the family joining us in the rising heat of the morning, clutching black coffees and wincing at the piercing shrieks of the wild turkeys. It had been a great family party last night and the meeting with the in-laws had gone well. Suddenly there is an enormous clap of thunder and a tropical rainstorm hits the deck. The palm trees are bending double and the sea is whipping up in a frenzy of foam.

No matter.

The phone goes again. Has no one picked up those roses yet?

I suppose we should get dressed soon. Anyone for another coffee first?

Andy gives me one of his great big bear hugs.

No more sadness.

No worries.

Byron Bay has entered my soul.

A FAVOURITE THING

Upon my bed there lies each day
A woolly sheep.
He's not a winsome lassie's toy,
He represents my youngest boy
Who sadly left these troubled shores
In search of peace,
Many moons ago.

His childhood curls earned him the name
Of Woolly Bear.
His cheerful smile warmed all he met.
His friends adored him here, and yet
He could not bear to listen more
To sounds of strife
In the land he loved.

His nickname led to many pranks
Concerning sheep.
His room was filled with objets d'art
All sheeply shaped, from near and far.
It seemed just right that he should choose
To go to Oz,
Land of sheep and sun.

He's been there now for twelve long years,
Our Woolly Bear.
He's found his peace and love and mate.
So why's this matted mutt so great?
The day he left this place I found
There on my bed
He'd laid his best-loved sheep.